FOLKLORE OF THE SCOTS

BY

SEANACHAIDH — The tale-teller

Also available in this series:

- Legends of the Clans.
- Giants of Loch Shiel and other Scottish Tales.
- The Fairy Mound and other Scottish Tales.

A full and updated publication list is available from the publishers on request:

Seanachaidh Presentations Ltd.,
Unit 44, Industrial Estate,
Port Glasgow, Inverclyde PA14 5XS.

Published 1986 by Seanachaidh Presentations Ltd.

ISBN 0 948963 05 0.

Typset by: Scottish I.T. Resource Centre, Print Studio, 19 Elmbank Street, Glasgow, Scotland.
Printed and bound by: Bell and Bain, Burnfield Road, Glasgow, Scotland.

Retold from the Scottish oral tradition with the publisher's special thanks to J. M. Fullerton, T. Macdonald, S.C.B.L. and A. Watson.

Seanachaidh Presentation Ltd. wishes to thank everyone who has been involved in turning the idea for this project into a reality. We also wish to thank our many friends who have given of their valuable time and skills.

Thanks also go to:

> W. Mason, A. McReynolds, L. Lindsay, A. Douglas, T. Rodger, A. Munn, D. Ward, R. Thompson, J. Pearce, J. Robertson, H. McLean. J. McCabe, T. Macdonald, P. Slater, A. Anglim and E. Hamilton.

Seanachaidh Presentations Ltd. is a registered charity.
Charity Registration No. ED 779/85
Details of membership can be sent on request.

Seanachaidh

Throughout the long and varied history of Scotland, there has always been a vast wealth of folklore and tradition.

The tales told by the old story teller — or Seanachaidh — have, for hundreds (and maybe even thousands) of year, been told around the firesides in the many small villages throughout the lowlands, the highlands and the islands.

Many a seanachaidh, it has been said, could tell a score of tales every night from the beginning of winter to its end — without once running short of a story to tell. The Seanachaidh would not read the stories, for many could not read. They were committed to memory and passed down orally from one generation to the next. Down through the ages of Scotland's history to the present day.

Seanachaidh Presentations bring alive that great oral tradition of Scottish Folklore and history once again. Many of the tales you will hear are true. Others . . . .? Well that's for you to decide as we reach back to a time **almost** gone and snatch a sound or two from a great and noble past.

The Seal Princesses

On the shores of Loch Duich stands the village of Dornie. The people of the village have, for many a year, made their living from the fishing grounds there. But none have made a catch quite like that of the widower Logue and his three sons.

Since the death of his wife, old Jamie Logue had nagged his three sons to be wed. The lads just did not seem able to do anything for themselves. The looking after them had sent their mother to an early grave and Jamie was determined, though he loved them dearly, to see them settled with wives before he followed her.

The lads all spent many an evening in the company of women, laughing and drinking and dancing. But they met not one whom they would take to be a wife. "Perhaps after ten years of searching without success, we can assume that the wives you are looking for do not exist," said old Jamie.

"Ach, it's easy for you to say, Father," said his eldest son. "You married the only decent woman this place has ever seen. If we could only find one like her, then we would marry her straight away."

"Oh you're too fussy by far," said Jamie. "I doubt a good woman would not have you, even if such a woman could be found."

One day, the Logues set out to fish as usual, off the coast of Skye. Almost immediately a sudden weight in their net threatened to capsize their small boat. "Cut the lines, Father!" shouted one son.

"I'll do no such thing!" replied old Jamie. One of you help me pull her in gently, while the others take the strain." They hauled the net in and were amazed to see that it was not full of fish, but contained three beautiful white seals.

Now fisherfolk, particularly those of the West, would normally release creatures at once, for they can be a superstitious people. Seals abound on the stony outcrops of the more remote parts of Scotland and it is believed that, at times, they will shed their skins and come ashore and dance in the moonlight as very beautiful men and women. When morning comes they will don their skins again and go back to the sea.

"Oh father," cried the youngest son. "We must put them back."

But his father was in no mood for advice. "I will not!" he cried. "Can you imagine what a price these skins will fetch? Get them skinned at once, you daft boys."

"But father . . . .!"

"Must I do everything myself?" stormed old Jamie. And pulling the first seal towards him, he took out his knife and ran it firmly down the seal's underside. Jamie and his sons gasped. From the opening he had made in the large white seal, a beautiful girl had flopped out onto the deck. "My God," cried Jamie. "I have never seen the like."

As the terrified girl tried to keep herself covered in the skin, Jamie did the same to the other two seals. For a long while he and his sons stared in wonder at the three beautiful girls, then at last Jamie found his tongue: "They are Seal Princesses — they must be! And you shall have them as wives." Now Tom, the youngest son, ran down to the cabin and fetched blankets to cover the Princesses. Then they headed for home. They gave the Princesses clothes which had belonged to their mother, then locked them in a bedroom and discussed what they should do next.

If the boys were to have as wives, explained Jamie, they must make sure the Princesses could never find their skins again for at the first opportunity, they would be away back where they had come from. So, the next day, the boys took the skins to a cove many miles from the village and weighted them with rocks and threw them into a deep pool. They then returned home to start work on the building of the houses that they would need. For their father's house was far too small now.

The marriages took place. But things were never as the boys would have liked. Despite all their efforts to make the Princesses happy, their wives always fretted to return home to their own families. It was Tom, the youngest and always the kindest, who could stand his wife's sorrow no longer. One day he gave in to her and fetched her skin from its hiding place. Sadly he watched as she slid gracefully into the waves. His two brothers called him a fool, of course. He would never find a wife to replace that one, they told him. Then they fetched the other skins in case Tom had betrayed the secret place.

A week went by — a week in which Tom had not left his house. Then, one evening, there was a knock at his door and there stood his wife. She explained that during their months together she had grown fond of Tom for his kindness and tenderness towards her. She stayed the night but was gone in the morning. Many a time in the months that followed, she would appear and stay the night, only to be gone with the dawn. Then, after a long absence, she arrived again. This time she was not alone. She had with her a fine baby boy. The child loved his father and looked forward to the frequent visits as much as his mother did. Not so with the children of Tom's brothers. They had never taken to their fathers and spent all their days playing in the loch.

One day, the children were visiting their grandfather, old Jamie. They were exploring the house, when they found a barrel in a bedroom cupboard. A bulky bundle lay at the bottom, hidden by old rags. The children lifted out the bundle and knew immediately what it was. They had been told many times by their mothers to watch out for the skins which could take them away from these dreary humans.

The brothers returned from the fishing with their day's catch late in the afternoon but went home to empty houses. After searching their own homes they went straight to old Jamie's and immediately their worst fears were confirmed.

They never saw their wives or their children again, although Tom was able to tell them any news he got from his wife, for they continued to love each other and met often. Tom felt sorry for his brothers and remembered his own sorrow when he had given his own princess her freedom. But he knew that their sorrow would last so much longer than his.

The Seer's Warning

Some time ago, the innkeeper of a lonely inn, near the ferry-crossing to Skye, was renowned for having second sight. All the people of the district knew of this but, as is usual, no one would speak of it nor even admit to the truth of it.

A man and his wife stayed at the inn one night. They were travelling to visit friends on Skye and, having missed the last ferry that night, decided to spend the night at the inn. The following morning they rose early to a thunderous storm. The morning was still pitch dark for such an early hour but they were determined to make an early start. On hearing this, the inn-keeper took them aside and told them of his power of second sight. He also told them that on three consecutive nights he had 'seen' the death of a man and woman. "They drowned in the sea," he said "When their small carriage broke away from their horse and plunged off the road."

When the inn-keeper had finished warning them, the couple stared at him. Then they looked at each other and smiled. The husband turned to the inn-keeper again and announced, "I am not from the highlands but I have heard tell of this second sight. I thank you for the warning you have given us, but I must say that such a thing can be nothing short of a bad dream on your part." The man looked again at his wife and, smiling once more, they were off with the words, "We have come a long way to visit dear friends and we cannot postpone our journey on the evidence of one man's dream."

Late that afternoon, news came to the inn-keeper that his two guests from the previous night had been pulled from the freezing sea only a few hundred yards from the inn.

"The horse must have separated from the carriage," he was told, "and the man, woman and carriage just plunged from the road into the raging sea below."

The inn-keeper just looked at the bearer of the tragic news and said, "Is that so? Who could ever have known?"

The Mermaid and the Fiddler

All of Tom's elder brothers were very good fiddlers. And his father? Well he was one of the best in the land. When any of them took up their fiddle and bow, and began to play, feet would start tapping and people would start dancing. There was always time for a Ceilidh when the fiddling began. But with Tom it was a different story. A different story altogether. You see, when young Tom played **his** fiddle the sound that came forth was a far cry from music. No matter how much he practised or how much his father or brothers tried to instruct him, the result was always the same. Screeeech . . . Screeeech . . . Screeeech was the very nearest thing to music that young Tom could manage. He would screeeech at parties and they would end abruptly. He would screeeech at dances and they would stop. And he would screeeech in private and even he could hardly stand the noise of it any longer. Try as he may, he just could not master the fiddling.

Anyway, after months and years of screechy practise, Tom's family became less and less sympathetic and more and more annoyed at his frantic attempts to master the fiddle playing. Eventually, he was barred from playing, or rather practising, indoors. Now, not wanting to give up his fiddling, young Tom began to practise away from the house and out of earshot. For weeks on end he wandered the hills and beaches around his home where he continued to practice, and continued to screeeech. He tried fast, then slow. He tried harder and more often. He tried to concentrate more, then he tried in a more abandoned way. He tried quietly and he tried loudly. But for all his trying his fiddling got not one bit better nor one step nearer to music. It would only produce the usual screeeech which scared all the birds and animals out of the district.

One day, as Tom wandered over the hills and down onto a small, isolated beach, he noticed something perched on one of the small rocks along the water's edge. At first he thought it was a big crow, but as he drew nearer he noticed it was bigger than a crow so he thought it might be a seal. Tom moved slowly and quietly towards the rock and, as he approached, he realised that the figure was not a crow or a seal but a beautiful mermaid which had come out of the sea to sun herself and comb her flowing silky hair.

Now Tom new of the magic powers of the mermaids and he sat behind one of the sand dunes to ponder the situation.

"Right," said Tom to himself. "First of all I must stay calm." You see not too many people have seen a mermaid and Tom was getting quite excited at the prospect of actually capturing one.

20

21

"Right," he said to himself again. "Stay calm and stay quiet then sneak up slowly, make a quick dash over the sand and catch her round the waist."

He peeked over the top of the sand dune and saw the mermaid sitting on the rock and looking out to sea, still combing her silky hair. He crawled over the edge of the dune, slid down onto the beach, and darted towards the rock by the water's edge. All the way across the beach he was sure the little mermaid would hear him approaching. But she did not. Tom made it right to where she sat. He flung his arms around her waist and clasped her tightly so that she was unable to wriggle free. And she did indeed wriggle. First she wriggled to her left, then to her right. Next she wriggled down the way, then she wriggled up. But Tom's grip on her was good and eventually the little mermaid gave up her struggle.

"Well Tom," she panted. "You caught me for sure." Tom was surprised that she knew his name, then he remembered the magic of the mermaids and that explained it.

"Yes, I caught you for sure," said Tom.

"For sure," said the mermaid. "But why?"

Tom thought for a minute or two. He knew of his chance of being granted a wish if he caught one.

"I've caught you for sure, have I not?" asked Tom.

"For sure," said the mermaid.

"I'll be entitled to a wish then, will I not?" asked Tom.

"For sure you will," said the mermaid. "But first you must release me."

Tom thought if he let her go she might escape. But the mermaid knew what his thoughts were.

"You've caught me for sure," she said, "and for sure you'll get your wish. That is the law and the tradition." So Tom released her cautiously. "Now," said the mermaid "what would you wish?"

"I wish to play the fiddle and to be good at playing the fiddle. That is my wish," said Tom.

"You want to be a fiddler do you?" said the mermaid.

"I do" says he.

Now, it was difficult for the mermaid to cast the right spell for she did not know how bad Tom's fiddle playing was. So she could hardly know how strong a spell she would have to cast. The mermaid asked Tom to play her a tune. He was a wee bit embarrassed but he lifted his fiddle and bow and began to play. Screeeech . . . Screeeech . . . Screeeech . . . . The mermaid winced at the sound of it all and Tom had to wince himself. "That'll take the strongest magic," said the mermaid.

"But can you do it?" pleaded Tom.

"For sure," said the mermaid. "But before

the wish is granted, and before the magic is done forever, you must answer me this. Do you want to play to please yourself or do you want to play to please others?'' Tom thought for a minute or two. He knew the standard of fiddling he wanted. Not just as good as other fiddlers in the district but his own **special** standard. That was what Tom wanted and that is what Tom would wish for. ''It must please me'' says Tom. ''My fiddling must please me.''

''It is done for sure'' says the mermaid, and she slipped away to her home in the sea.

Now Tom didn't **feel** any different. His fiddle and bow didn't **look** any different. But when he began to play, the sound was **very** different. He thought it was the sweetest music that a fiddle or fiddler had ever produced and he played and played until he was exhausted.

Tom knew that a big ceilidh was to be held that evening and, if he hurried, he'd have the chance to let everyone hear his lovely music. He had a fair way to go but he arrived at the ceilidh just in time. Without any hesitation he started to play and was delighted with the sound that he heard. The bow almost floated across the strings and his fingers danced along the stock. The music he made was the best he'd ever heard and Tom was very, very pleased. Alas, no others were pleased, for all they could hear was the screeeech, screeeech, screeeech of Tom's terrible fiddling. For though it sounded like heaven to Tom, only his perception of his fiddling had changed, not the fiddling itself.

This should be a lesson to us all. I for one, will

be very precise, if I ever have the good fortune
to catch a mermaid.

The Witch's Death

Old Alan had been a shepherd all his life. As he wandered the hills with his sheep, he saw many a strange sight and was witness to many unusual happenings.

Alan was making his way home from the hillside pastures one wet and windy evening. He had just passed through the old churchyard and had not far to go before reaching the village. It was here that a very strange sight met him.

An old, clay-faced woman, with blood streaming from her face and neck, was running fast towards him. The wind snatched at her clothing and her cloak and hair flapped wildly.

She took no notice of the shepherd however, and hurried past in the direction of the old churchyard. Now, this would have been strange enough but, as old Alan walked on, two huge, black dogs thundered past — seemingly in pursuit of the old woman. Behind the dogs rode a dark stranger on horseback — as dark as a moonless night.

It was indeed very strange . . . but, as I have said, old Alan had seen many strange things in his long life on the lonely hills, so he put the scene behind him and made haste towards the village.

Alan soon reached his small cottage and hurriedly told his wife the story of the old bloodied woman. When he had finished he sat back, pleased with himself for having told such a strange and eerie tale. But the old shepherd's wife was hardly impressed. "I too have a tale to tell," she announced. "It happened today and although I was not involved myself, I have all the details. It will be of interest to you my husband, for it will explain your woman, dogs and horseman."

"Then tell your tale," said Alan abruptly. He was not a little put out at having his fine story overshadowed by another. "Tell your tale," he repeated, "and I will surely listen." So Alan's wife began to tell of the news in the village that very day.

"Will you know of Iain Dubh, or Black John the Hunter as he is known?" asked Alan's wife of him. Alan nodded. "And you will know of his great hatred of those workers of the Devil, the Witches?" Again the old shepherd nodded and his wife continued with her story.

"Well," she said, "Iain Dubh went hunting today and, as usual, he took with him those two great dogs of his. He went deep into the hills in search of the great Red Stag, but the weather was very bad and he was forced to give up the hunt and to seek shelter in the old bothy by the 'Whistling Forest.'

"Now, he had just managed to light the bothy fire and had settled down with his dogs to rest when he heard a scratching noise at the bothy door. At first he thought it was just the storm but again he heard a distinct scratching and so he went to see what it was. As Iain went to the door and opened it to the storm outside, a small black cat brushed past him into the room. It was all that he could do to keep his two dogs off the poor animal. Suddenly, the cat spoke to Iain — as I am speaking to you now. It begged him to have mercy and told him that the Witch of Laggan herself had turned her from a poor farm maiden into a pathetic little cat with no home and no shelter.

"Now, this little cat had an eerie, little voice and Iain suspected a witch's trick. But as he listened to the cat's moaning and looked down at the wretched creature before him, his heart took pity and he agreed to help it he could. The little cat thanked him for his kindness and spoke to him again. 'I am quite frightened of those ferocious dogs you have. Is there no way you could tie them? It would make me feel much safer as I dry myself by the fire.'

"The wind howled fiercely from outside the lonely bothy and Iain's pity grew stronger. So he took his two dogs and tied them to a beam in the corner of the room. No sooner had he done so than the little black cat began to grow to an enormous size. Its fur became spiked and the eyes shot red with anger and hatred. The huge beast flashed its filthy, gruesome fangs and screamed, 'This is the penalty you pay for your hatred and persecution of witches.'

"The bothy shook from the force of the creature's screams and it flew at Iain's throat. He could **smell** death itself from the animal's breath as it spat out its oaths and scratched at him. Blood flowed red from the deep gashes it made in his face and the claws and fangs ripped into his head and shoulders.

"The two dogs strained at their ropes but the knots only tightened. But, as the big cat lunged at Iain's throat, the beam splintered under the strain of the dogs and they pounced on the cat-witch. They bit and tore at her to save their master, but, even so, she managed to escape, her fur and flesh ripped as they were.

"Now Iain is a brave and strong hunter and he managed to make his way home to the village. When he told his story the villagers told him of the old crone in the next village who had been attacked by wolves that very same day.

"Without waiting for his injuries to be treated, Iain made his way to the cottage in the village of Laggan and saw the victim of the wolves

But Iain knew that the torn flesh around her throat had been done by no wolf. 'This is the witch who attacked me and these are the marks of my dogs on her throat!' announced Iain. As the old witch died, Iain Dubh the Hunter was well pleased with his day's work."

Now all this time old Alan the shepherd had listened to the fearful tale told by his wife. But he could not understand what it had to do with his own experience that day. "But what of the old woman, the dogs **and** the rider?" he asked.

"Twas the spirit of the cat-witch at the moment of her death, fleeing to the church for sanctuary. The dogs were those of Iain Dubh, and the rider — Auld Nick himself. Their aim was to stop the cat-witch reaching the sanctuary of the Kirk, and so depriving the devil of her black soul."

The Bridge of gold

The Dornoch Firth bites deep into Scotland's North-east coast. A great many years ago the shores of the Firth gave shelter and homes to a large band of Fairy Folk. They plied their various crafts around the Firth and traded with others for gold — of which they had vast stores.

But the Fairy traders had constant problems with their small cockleshell — and sometimes even eggshell — boats. The two major problems they faced were the high winds and the strong currents. Anyway, they got quite fed up with all the rowing and decided one day that they should build a bridge across the Dornoch Firth between Ross-shire in the South and Sutherland in the North. Not only did they decide to build a bridge, but they also decided it would be the most lavish and beautiful bridge to be found anywhere. They agreed therefore that the bridge across the Firth would be built with nothing less than gold.

The Fairies chose their spot carefully and brought together the very best of their

33

goldsmiths and builders. They also gathered together their vast stores of gold, melted it down in the fairy-furnaces and had their smiths turn it all into the strongest of building materials. When everything was prepared, they set to work on the most amazing golden bridge ever to be seen.

Now, everyone knows that the Fairies live in everlasting fear of the name of God reaching their ears. Simply uttering the name within hearing distance is enough to stop them for sure in anything they may be doing at the time; regardless of whether they are engaged in good work, as on this occasion, or engaged in mischief which is usually the way of it.

Anyway, the Fairies gathered their gold, and the Bridge across the Firth began to take shape. But one day, when they were working diligently on one of the big spans, a stranger to the district happened to pass by on his journey northward. He rested for a while to watch what he thought was an ordinary bridge built by ordinary men and women. But he was so overawed by the gleaming construction that he could not help himself from exclaiming: "God bless those who are involved in **that** piece of workmanship."

No sooner had the unfortunate words been uttered than all the little fairy folk jumped into their cockleshell boats and made off towards the open sea — never to be seen in that district again.

Today there is a sandbank running South to North across the Dornoch Firth. No one knows for certain what caused such a build-up of sand at that precise spot.

The Wedding Guest

Lachlan was in love. Anyone could see, the way he skipped along, singing and whistling wherever he went. For a grown man the size of Lachlan, skipping did not come easy. But on he pranced along the side of the forest to talk with the minister at the manse.

"Would you just slow down." shouted Alan. "The minister will still be there. There's no need for all this skipping and jumping." Alan was to be the Best Man at the Wedding. He had been Lachlan's friend since they were children. But since Lachlan had won the heart of that girl from the next village he had changed. He had been a quiet, solemn man who spoke only when it suited him. But now, with love in his heart, he'd been turned into a child again. It was all very exasperating for Alan right enough.

Lachlan reached the corner of the kirkyard and waited there for Alan. "My . . . she's a beauty Alan. Is she not?"

"She is that but there is no need to run all the

way to the manse. Just take your time and we'll get there just the same.''

"I've not felt like this before, Alan. Is it normal, do you think?''

"Well, I wouldn't quite say it was normal. Not for you anyway, Lachlan. The villagers think you've gone quite mad, you know, and it scares them a bit.''

"Scared of me.'' laughed Lachlan, "I'm nothing to be scared of.''

"A bearded giant skipping down the village main street as you do can be frightening, you know. I can understand it, being your friend and all. But it would be better if you just slowed down now and again. You are in grave danger of burning yourself out before your wedding night.''

"That's not true.'' protested Lachlan.

"Truth it is.'' said Alan. "Now, let's go to the manse and make the arrangements. We'll go through the kirkyard here.''.

Lachlan managed to slow himself down and Alan managed to keep up with him. But as they walked through the gravestones of the kirkyard they noticed that some of the stones had toppled in the high winds. Lachlan leaned down to replace one of them and read out the name of the deceased. "John McNeil,'' he read aloud. "Well, John McNeil, if you were not so dead I'd have you at my wedding.'' And he replaced the stone. Alan was furious at this disrespect and told Lachlan that such a thing should not be done, even in jest.

"I'm sorry, Alan," replied Lachlan. It's just my joy. But if that John McNeil was here, I'd invite him right enough." And at that he rushed ahead again to be away from Alan's scolding.

With everything well arranged, Lachlan was wed to the sweetheart he loved so much. They left the church and a fine wedding ceilidh was held in the house of Lachlan's parents. Everyone was happy and the food and the whisky was enough and more.

Now, as the piping and dancing and the ceilidh continued, the darkness fell on the village and a loud rapping noise was heard at the door of the house. A stranger stood there, head bowed to the howling wind, and asked that Lachlan should come with him quickly to another house nearby. Thinking the stranger was in need of assistance, Lachlan agreed and followed the stooping man along the track in the darkness of the night. It was not long before they reached the house the stranger spoke of and they entered at once. It was a strange house, old and dusty as if no one really lived there anymore. Lachlan looked around and strained his eyes, for the only light came from a candle on the dusty table at which the stranger had now sat himself.

"And what is the problem I can help you with?" asked Lachlan.

"There is no problem," said the stranger. "I only wished to attend your wedding and to speak to you."

"Then come and I will introduce you to my friends."

"In a while," insisted the stranger. "First, be seated so that I can talk. And when the candle burns out we will go." Lachlan looked at the candle. It was well used and would not last more than a few minutes. He sat across the table and the stranger began to speak.

"My name is John." he said. "I once lived in this small cottage and worked in the fields at the back of here. I have not been here for many years and it is good to be back . . ." The stranger continued with his talk, none of which held any interest for Lachlan. For he had many guests and a new wife along the road and he wished to be gone from this dull place.

The stranger talked on, ". . . and my family has long since left here now," he said. "It is a great pity that none of them are left. But see, the candle is almost gone. You should leave now Lachlan, and be with your family."

At that the candle flickered but the room did not become dark. The early morning sun had just risen and Lachlan remembered his wife and friends and was gone.

As he rushed back to the little ceilidh, he didn't notice the changes in the village from the night before. He reached the open door of his parent's house and stepped inside. An old woman was sweeping dust with her broom. "Where are my family and my friends? And my wife?" asked Lachlan. He explained to the old woman about the wedding, and the Ceilidh and about the stranger.

"I have no knowledge of your family." said the woman. But you remind me of a story my grandmother told me. She had been a bridesmaid at her friend's wedding and as the families danced and sang, the bridegroom left the house with a stranger never to return."

"You are a fool," said Lachlan. "It was my wedding. It was here last evening and, of course, I've returned."

"But that cannot be," explained the old woman with the broom, "for the wedding I speak of was only a tale from my grandmother's youth. A hundred years ago, it would be." And she turned away from Lachlan and carried on sweeping the room.

As the rays of the morning sun found the doorway of the house, Lachlan fell to the floor as dust upon the threshold and the old woman continued with her sweeping.

A Ghostly Challenge

I consider myself fortunate to have met with disbelievers on only a few, rare occasions. It is usually an unpleasant experience for all concerned. Unpleasant for us who know better and unpleasant for those whose arrogance leads them to accept our challenge of proof.

Some time ago a tailor came to this small village of ours. He was a good man and a good tailor too, that grand combination of gentleman and craftsman. He did a fine trade throughout the parish because of his skills and he settled in quite well, for a stranger.

After a short while, no more than a few months to be exact, the tailor arrived back from a visit to a neighbouring village. He was weary from his walk over the hills and went straight to the well to quench his thirst. A few of the older villagers were also at the well, evidently enjoying the spring sunshine. The tailor drank, rested and spoke to the villagers of his walk and of his weariness from it. "It is surely a fine day but the sun is just a bit too hot for such a strenuous walk," he said. "I rested only once

41

at the old kirkyard. If I'd stopped more often I'd not be feeling as tired as I do now."

"The old kirkyard?" said one of the company. "You timed the passing of that place well. It's not a spot for resting after dark." The others slowly nodded in agreement.

But our fine tailor only smiled at them, "A kirk is a kirk by day or by night. You would surely not have me believe the contrary." And so the discussion continued with the villagers giving their testimony, one be one, about the old kirk and the ghost who haunted it and the tailor continued to smile at their superstitious nonsense. It was not long before both sides knew that there would be no end to the debate unless some greater proof was sought. The tailor was therefore challenged to go to the old Kirk at midnight and to fetch back the skull which stood by the window there. But to the surprise and delight of everyone, the tailor smiled more broadly than before. "I will go to the kirk this very night and remain there till tomorrow's sun rises and to keep away the boredom, I will sew a pair of trews whilst there."

As the evening darkness crept over the village, the tailor made his way to the old Kirk once more. He was a brave man, that at least must be said, as he whistled merrily and picked his way through the ancient head stones and into the ruins of the building. By this time it was almost midnight and, with only a candle for light, the tailor settled himself beside a crumbling window to begin his work on the trews.

To begin with, he cut his cloth and laid it

before him on a large flat stone. Then, piece by piece, he took them up and carefully stitched them together. As he worked he whistled and sang to himself, taking great care to choose only the gayest of all the songs he knew. Midnight came and was gone again, and the tailor sewed diligently on in his own expert way. He knew he need not fear the childish superstitions of the villagers and looked forward to the rising sun and an end to this silly game.

Shortly after midnight had passed however, the tailor sensed a movement by the wall opposite him. He glanced quickly toward the base of the wall but all was still, so he continued his sewing and continued with his merry songs. But again he was distracted from his work by a scratching noise by the wall.

He had thought before that it had been the flickering candle that had caused the sense of movement. But candles don't make scratching noises and as the tailor looked across the old Kirk for a second time, he saw that the earth beside a headstone was being slowly disturbed.

He looked away and hurriedly returned to stitching the trews. The scratching continued and the earth moved more violently than before. Small pieces of the ground erupted and, as the tailor stared toward the disturbance, a filthy, bony hand broke the surface of the the grave.

"Look at the old mouldy hand, tailor. The mouldy, meatless hand, tailor!" announced a dreadful, muffled voice from the grave.

The tailor shivered with fear. "I see the hand

43

but I sew the trews." he replied, and continued with his task.

The earth shook harder still, and as the brave tailor watched, a grisly shoulder and chest was forced to the surface. "Look at the old mouldy chest, tailor. The mouldy, meatless chest, tailor." announced the fearful voice from the grave.

Almost terrified, the tailor again gave his reply, "I see the chest but I will sew the trews." And he quickened his pace and lengthened his stitches. He was shaking uncontrollably and wished he had never scoffed at the warning he had been given. But he had boasted of finishing the trews and finish them he must.

The earth rumbled and the grave opened wider and wider. The haunch and legs, caked with dirt and grime, pushed over the edge. "Look at the mouldy legs, tailor." boomed the evil, unearthly voice. "The mouldy, meatless legs tailor."

As the tailor looked toward the open grave he continued to sew. "I see the legs," he stammered with fright, but I sew the trews." His stitches lengthened still more as his hand shook terribly.

"Look at the mouldy corpse, tailor." bellowed the voice. "The mouldy, meatless corpse, tailor." And as the walls of the old Kirk trembled the corpse arose from its tomb.

The tailor looked and, with a shaking rasping voice, shouted back, "I see your corpse and I sew these trews." But as the mouldy, meatless

45

form lunged toward him he broke off his final stitch and fled. The corpse pursued him and howled its terrible oaths as it gained on the tailor who had nearly reached the doorway.

Almost upon him the rotted, foul corpse aimed a blow that fortunately missed its mark and thudded into the door-post instead. And as the tailor fled from the ruined Kirk, the building was struck by the first rays of the morning sun, the cock crowed in the village, and the ground closed over the corpse as he returned to his tomb.

To this day, the imprint of the dead man's blow remains at the entrance to the old Kirk as a reminder to others of the traditional challenge of proof that is sought from the disbeliever.

The Giants
of
Loch Shiel

It was a hard life living on the shores of Loch Shiel. If it wasn't bad enough that the land was covered by huge boulders, so that no-one could farm it, in the hills above the Loch lived two of the most noisy, quarrelsome giants that ever lived.

Each believed that he was the biggest and strongest giant in the whole of Scotland, and every day and night the village shook to the bangings and crashings of the giants' constant quarelling. No-one wanted to leave the village though. It was their home, but they were very poor and despairing of their plight.

Every week the men of the village met to discuss ideas on how to move the boulders from their land, so that they could farm it and become as prosperous as their neighbours in other places. But no matter how clever the scheme, no matter how many of the strongest men tried, the huge rocks still remained stubbornly planted in the ground.

All might have been lost, for the people were at their wits' end, but one day the mysterious

Euan left his home at the edge of the village and came to a village meeting.

When he stood to speak, those present fell silent, for Euan was a strange man whose solitary life of study and prayer had made him very wise and greatly respected by local folk. In a quite gentle voice he announced that he had a plan which would, at one swoop, solve all their problems. It would clear the land and rid them of those troublesome giants.

The men were disbelieving but they had nothing to lose so, when Euan set out to bring back the miracle they needed, he carried with him the best wishes of every person in the village, even though they had no idea what he was going to do. Secretive indeed was our Euan. And no wonder. If he had told the villagers that the giants would clear away the boulders they would have laughed at him all the way to Inverness, such was the madness of his idea.

Euan, travelling alone, soon reached the caves where the giants lived side by side but, as usual, they were in the middle of a fierce argument. So Euan settled on a rock and waited to be noticed. At last they spotted him and were shocked into silence at the impudence of this tiny human coming to them. Euan, however, was a brave man and, as he spoke, they recognised the strength in his gentle voice, and listened.

"Why always argue?" he asked them. "Will you spend all eternity arguing? I have an idea as to how you can settle this quarrel." That captured the dreadful giants' interest and they

listened closely.

Euan's return to the village was greeted joyously by the villagers but they froze in horror when they saw the two giants in the distance behind him. Euan went straight to the council and explained that the giants would have a trial of strength on the Shores of Loch Shiel the next day. They would each lift the huge boulders from the land and hurl them as far as they could. The winner would be the one who threw the most rocks.

When morning arrived, all the villagers stood in the fields to watch this awesome contest. All day the giants lifted and threw, lifted and threw. But when night fell, though all the boulders had gone, the giants began to argue again, for both had thrown the same number and there were none left. There was no winner. Terrified by the noise the villagers ran home, for the giants were more fearsome close to than they had been in the hills.

Only Euan remained. He put the second part of his plan into action. "Well, you both threw the same number so obviously the winner must be the one who threw the boulder furthest. Go out and search for the boulder lying furthest away so that I may declare a winner."

Who won has never been discovered because, since then, no-one on the shores of Loch Shiel has seen, or heard, a giant. Have you?

The Islay Smithy

There once lived a blacksmith on Islay who had a son. The boy grew into a sturdy youth of great liveliness then, suddenly, at the age of thirteen he fell ill. His skin turned yellow and wrinkled and he never stirred from his bed. The 'smith was almost out of his mind with worry, since the boy showed no signs of improving and no cure could be found, so in desperation he sought the advice of a local wise man.

The old man came to the forge and looked closely at the young boy. He thought deeply for some time and then told the 'smith that it was not his son who was in the bed, but a changeling, someone the fairies had put there in place of his son. To make certain that this was the case, the old man told the 'smith how to put his theory to the test.

The 'smith set about building a big peat fire in the hearth in accordance with the old man's instructions. He got together a dozen eggshells, filled them with water, and arranged them around the fire in full view of the one on the bed. The changeling shrieked with laughter at

51

these absurd proceedings and cried out: "In all my 500 years, I've not seen anything as silly as this." At this, the 'smith grabbed hold of the old fairy and with all his might flung him into the flames. Instantly, there was a great blinding flash, whereupon the changeling disappeared up the chimney.

Convinced now that the fairies had carried off the 'smith's son, the wise man set his mind to the task of getting him back. He felt sure that the boy was being held captive inside a local fairy mound, which usually lay open only once a year, on the night of Hallowe'en.

The wise man told the 'smith his plan and, realising that this was his only chance of getting his son back, the 'smith bravely made his preparations. On the night of Hallowe'en, he set out for the fairy mound taking with him a dirk, a bible and a cockerel as he had been instructed.

As he drew near the fairy mound the 'smith saw that it was open and brightly lit up. The ground beneath his feet seemed to tremble with the sound of music and dancing which could be heard from within. Remembering the advice of the old man, the 'smith took heart and gathering his courage together he walked boldly up to the open door. He stuck his dirk in the doorpost, for he knew that the steel would prevent the door from closing and locking him inside Holding his bible tightly, to protect him from any fairy harm, he strode into the mound and demanded the return of his son.

At this, the fairies grew angry and then they

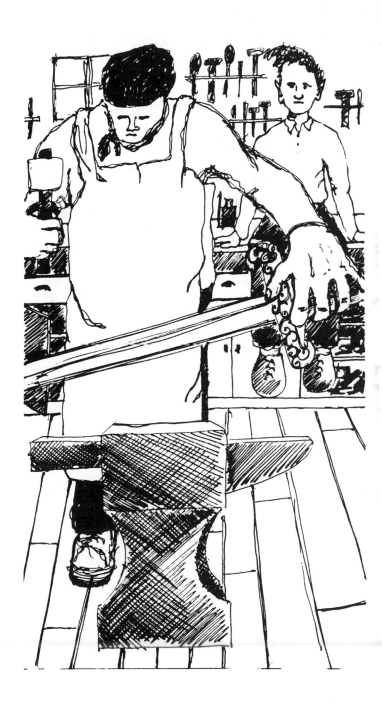

began to laugh at the poor old 'smith. They laughed and laughed, mocking and jeering him until their wild laughter wakened the cockerel, which had been asleep in the 'smith's arms. Now everyone knows that all fairy fun must cease at cockcrow and, as the cockerel crowed loudly and flapped its wings, the fairies disappeared into the depths of the mound. The 'smith took this opportunity and, seizing his son, he fled, taking the dirk from the door as he went.

For a year and a day after this, the boy did nothing but eat and sleep but, one day, he was watching his father in the forge, at work on a sword for the clan chief. Aware of the importance of his task, the 'smith laboured long and hard, but, try as he might, he was unable to finish the sword to his satisfaction. Suddenly the boy announced, "That's not the way to do it. Let me show you." The boy then made the most perfect sword ever.

The sword was presented to the Lord of the Isles and its reputation was such that everyone wanted a sword from the Islay blacksmith and his son, never knowing that the boy had learned his trade from the fairies.

The Two
Tale tellers

For many years throughout the district, Dougie and Archie were well known for the many tall tales they could tell. They were always entertaining stories but the local people would often give an unhappy sigh when the two old worthies launched into their tale-telling.

They would sigh for three reasons. The first reason was that Dougie and Archie never told stories about other people. It was always themselves who were the heroes. For they claimed — and their claims were always consistent — that the encounters with fairies, witches, ghosts and seal people which they told of, were nothing short of the absolute truth.

Now, if this was indeed the case, then Archie and Dougie certainly did not lead a normal life. According to them, they had both been turned into a score of different creatures at the hands of the witches. They had had terrifying experiences with ghosts and had even managed, on some occasions, to strike fear and terror into the ghosts themselves. Aye, it must be said that Dougie and Archie were masters of their art — of exaggeration that is.

But the local people would sigh for another reason. For when Dougie would tell a great tale of an exceptional experience, then Archie would always tell of a better one. And when Archie had finished, Dougie would come back with something even better. So they were all the time in fierce competition, striving to come up with a better, more sinister, more frightening and more **truthful** new story.

The third reason for the many sighs was that the two tale-tellers were over fond of their whisky and could barely tell even the shortest story without the help of the great golden liquid. It was even said by some that the two of them had their own still somewhere in the hills — but that's another story.

This story concerns a number of strange events on the very night of Hallowe'en itself. Archie and Dougie were in the village inn as usual and, as usual, each was trying to come up with a better tale than the other; all of the time proclaiming the truth of it all; all of the time taking the whisky; and all of the time getting deeper into a heated argument because of it all. After a short time, there were fewer and fewer tales to be heard and more and more arguments. Eventually, the two of them drained their glasses and, still shouting bitterly at each other, staggered through the crowded inn and out into the village square, leaving everyone else behind to enjoy the remainder of the evening in peace.

Now, as I've said before, that was the night of Hallowe'en. The following night it was only

Archie who was seated in his favourite corner of the inn. He lifted the glass and drained it. The inn was busy but everyone was silent, for no one had ever seen Archie or Dougie on their own. "And where might Dougie be tonight?" asked the innkeeper of Archie. "He'd not be ill would he?"

Old Archie looked at the innkeeper. His eyes dashed round the faces of everyone standing around him, waiting to hear some news of his friend. "If Dougie Baird is ill," said Archie, "then I'll not be knowing it. And if he's dead," he continued, "then I'll not be knowing that either. Whatever happened to that fool Dougie is only to be blamed on himself." And at that, Archie replenished his glass and took another long, shaking gulp.

As Archie sat alone in his corner, nursing his drink, speculation started amongst the other customers and, before he finished his sixth glass — which was not too long a time — Archie was confronted by the local constable and a fairly hostile crowd.

"Now, Archie Graham," said the big constable in the manner constables do, "I am trying to locate your friend, Dougie Baird, and I'll be asking you now where he might be." Archie ordered another drink and it was laid before him on the table. Another was laid before the constable who shook his head in refusal then drained the glass. "Right," said the constable, "where might I find Dougie Baird?"

"You might find him at home, but I doubt it." said Archie. "Or you might find him in Hell itself which is a more likely place I'll be thinking." And he looked straight into the constable's eyes. "You can believe it or you can disbelieve it but what happened last night on Hallowe'en was terrible and I will tell you the whole story when the glass is filled."

The glass was filled once more and Archie told his story to the constable and all who gathered around him. When he had finished his account he sat back in his chair and waited. There was

a deathly silence in the inn until the constable began to speak. His voice had changed from that of a gruff lawman to that of an even gruffer lawman and he leaned across the table and glowered at Archie.

"You would have me believe **that?**" said the constable. "You are trying to tell me, in front of these very witnesses that you were walking home with Dougie when you heard music and saw a light from the 'Round Hill' beyond the bridge. You say that you and Dougie went to investigate and discovered that the hill is really a Fairy Mound and that a hundred and more of the Little People were having a ceilidh and dancing to the sound of the pipes? Then, you say, because Dougie Baird was drunker even than you, he entered the Round Hill — my apologies, the Fairy Mound, joined in the dancing with the Fairies inside, and before you could persuade him to come out again, the hill closed over and he, with all those fairies, was gone? That is what you are asking me to believe happened?"

"Aye," said Archie and he was arrested.

Now, that might well have been the end of a long friendship and an end to the tale-telling in the village inn, for the sheriff did not believe Archie's story any more than the constable did and he was put in jail.

It was exactly a hundred and one nights from the night of Hallowe'en however, that Dougie Baird walked into the inn once more. He was still quite drunk and panting hard from much exercise. "Now," he announced to the silenced crowd, "If a glass is filled and put before me, I have a tale of the Fairies and myself to tell you all.''